LEARN NUMBERS
WITH DINOSAURS

www.aceacademicprep.com

Author: Ace Academic Publishing

Ace Academic Publishing is a leading supplemental educational workbook publisher for grades K-12. At Ace Academic Publishing, we realize the importance of imparting analytical and critical thinking skills during the early ages of childhood and hence our books include materials that require multiple levels of analysis and encourage the students to think outside the box.

The materials for our books are written by award winning teachers with several years of teaching experience. All our books are aligned with state standards and are widely used by many schools throughout the country.

For enquiries and bulk order, contact us at the following address:

3736, Fallon Road, #403
Dublin, CA 94568
www.aceacademicprep.com

 **Ace Academic Publishing**
ACHIEVING EXCELLENCE TOGETHER

ISBN: 978-1-949383-17-1

Parent's Guide

Use this book to introduce your child to the world of numbers. With fun dinosaur facts along the way, your child will be engaged and thrilled to learn the numbers! Not only that, you can use the colorful and exciting activities to play with your child while they learn to count and write the numbers.

Ace Academic Publishing
ACHIEVING EXCELLENCE TOGETHER

Other books from Ace Academic Publishing

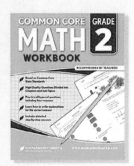
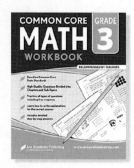
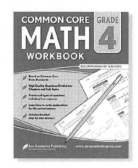

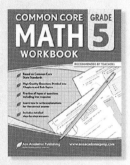

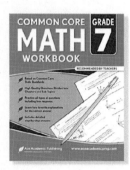
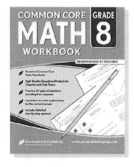

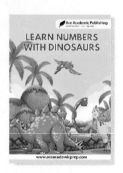

Ace Academic Publishing

ACHIEVING EXCELLENCE TOGETHER

DINOSAURS

HELLO EVERYONE!
WE ARE THE DINOSAUR FAMILY AND WE ARE EXCITED TO LEARN THE NUMBERS WITH YOU!

DID YOU ASK, "WHO ARE DINOSAURS?"

OK THEN, WE WILL SHARE A LOT OF FUN FACTS ABOUT OUR FAMILY WHILE LEARNING THE NUMBERS WITH YOU!

ARE YOU READY? LET'S GO!

1

Let's count 1 to 10!

Color me!

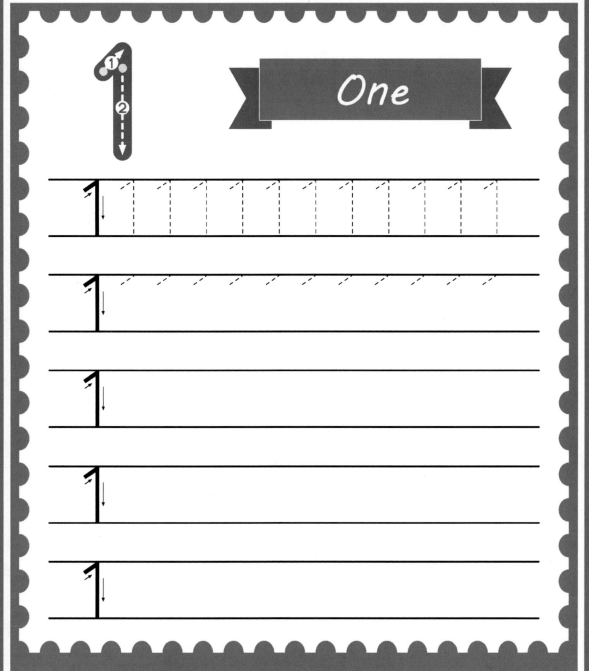

One

Richard Owen created the word dinosaur, meaning "fearfully-great lizard" in 1842.

Flying Dinosaur

Pterosaurs were one of the flying dinosaurs. Pterosaurs weren't dinosaurs themselves, but they were related to them.

They had wings made of skin and hollow bones that made flying easier.

Pterosaurs were the biggest flying creatures on earth. They grew upto 22 feet (10 meters).

Most of the Pterosaurs ate fish.

Two

2

2

2

2

2

Dinosaurs ruled the earth over 160 million years ago.

WHO DOES NOT FIT?

Circle me

8

Three

3 3 3 3 3 3 3 3

3

3

3

3

Dinosaurs lived during a period of time known as the Mesozoic Era, or Age of Reptiles.

Swimming Dinosaur

Spinosaurus is probably the biggest meat-eating dinosaur we know.

A Spinosaurus was similar to a crocodile which lived on land and in water (Amphibian).

Spinosaurus had webbed feet that were helpful for swimming and catching prey.

Spinosaurus might have eaten sharks and other large fish.

4 4 4 4 4 4 4

4 / / / / / / /

4

4

4

The first dinosaur was named the Megalosaurus in 1824.

Color me!

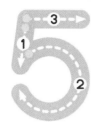

5 5 5 5 5 5 5 5 5

5 5 5 5 5 5 5 5 5

5

5

5

Everything we know about dinosaurs came from their *fossils*.

SHADOW
MATCHING GAME

Six

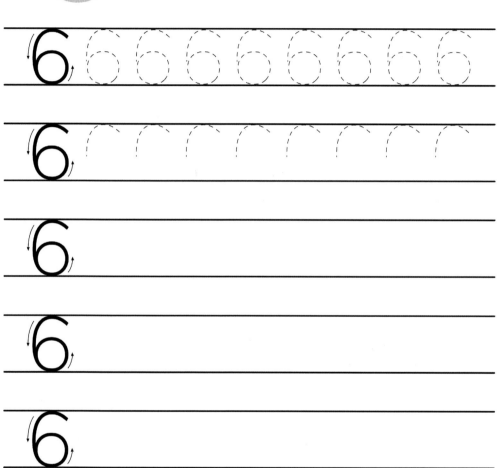

6 6 6 6 6 6 6 6 6 6

6

6

6

6

Dinosaur fossils have been discovered from all over the world. Scientists have found fossils even from Antarctica.

Interesting Dino Facts

A T-rex bite would have been more than two times as powerful as a lion's.

Most dinosaurs had long tails that helped them keep their balance while running.

Small meat eaters were probably the smartest kinds of dinosaurs.

Many scientists think that birds evolved (or came) from dinosaurs. This means that we have dinosaurs around us today!

Dinosaurs dominated the earth for over 165 million years. Humans have only been around for about 2 million years.

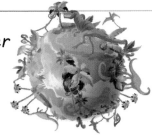

7

Seven

The study of ancient life is called Paleontology, and a scientist who studies it is called a Paleontologist.

How many T-Rexs are in each line?

8 8 8 8 8 8 8 8 8 8

8 0 0 0 0 0 0 0 0 0

8

8

8

The first dinosaur was discovered in 1854 by Ferdinand Vandiveer Hayden during his exploration on the Upper Missouri River.

Color me!

20

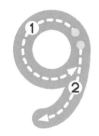

9 9 9 9 9 9 9 9 9 9

9 9 9 9 9 9 9 9 9

9

9

9

Most dinosaurs hatched from eggs.

Fill in the missing numbers!

22

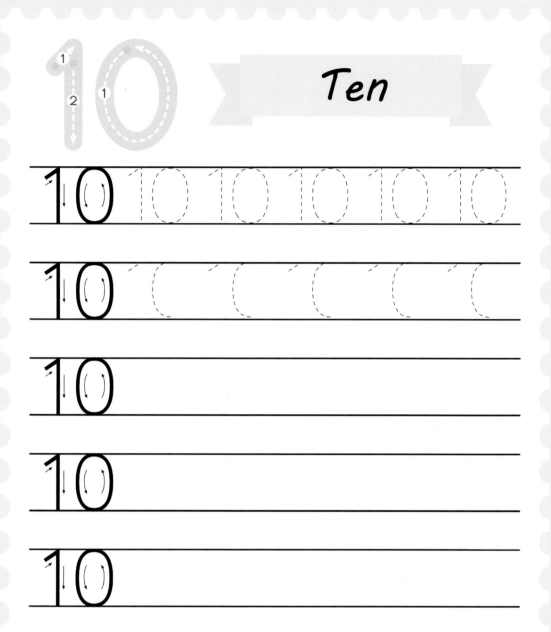

Ten

10 10 10 10 10 10

10

10

10

10

Dinosaur eggs came in different shapes and sizes. The Eggs were oval or round and anywhere between 3cm to 30 cm long!

ELEVEN

11

TWELVE

12

THIRTEEN

13

FOURTEEN

14

FIFTEEN

15

SIXTEEN

16

SEVENTEEN

17

EIGHTEEN

18

NINETEEN

19

TWENTY

20

Let's count from **11** to **20**!

11 12 13 14 15 16 17 18 19 20

Count how many dinosaurs are in each line! Write that number in the circle.

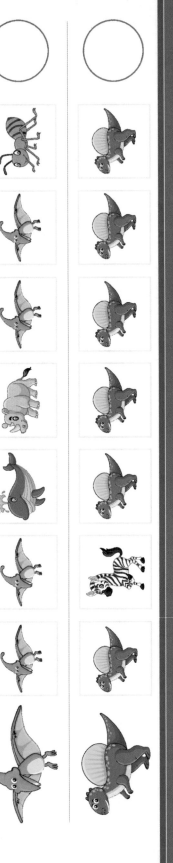

26

11 Eleven

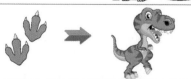

Dinosaur footprints can give us clues about the dinosaurs. For example, if the print is sharp-clawed, it's a carnivore. If it's got round toes, it's a herbivore.

The tallest, the heaviest and the smallest

Longest - The tallest dinosaur was Argentinosaurus. This massive dinosaur measured over 40 meters, as tall as four fire engines!

Heaviest - The heaviest dinosaur was also the Argentinosaurus! at 77 tons, it was the same weight as 17 African Elephants!

Smallest - The smallest fully-grown fossil dinosaur was the little bird-hipped, plant-eating lesothosaurus. It was only the size of a chicken!

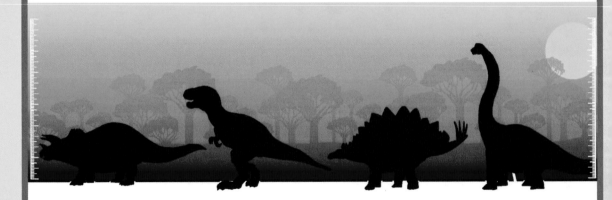

Twelve

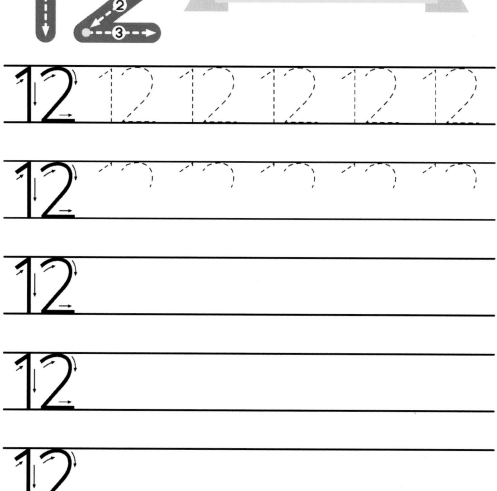

Two of the largest dinosaurs, *Brachiosaurus* and *Apatosaurus*, were both surprising herbivores!

Color me!

13

13 13 13 13 13 13

13

13

13

13

Some dinosaurs had natural weapons on their bodies, like the Triceratops. It had 3 horns on its head!

Can you help this Velociraptor!

			38	24	78	28	80	48	98
			79	57	8	9	10	58	90
			1	2	24	27	11	12	30
31	32	1	34	5	6	7	74	13	40
41	42	2	3	4	46	8	15	14	50
88	26	53	14	13	12	9	16	59	60
61	62	63	15	65	11	10	68	69	70
74	72	73	16	17	12	77			
81	82	83	84	85	13	14			
91	64	93	94	95	96	97			

Take him through the math maze so he can meet his friend!

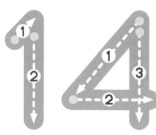

Fourteen

14 14 14 14 14 14 14

14

14

14

14

Corythosaurus had a big nose. This nose was used as an echo chamber, which helped Corythosaurus make a loud blast of sound.

Color me!

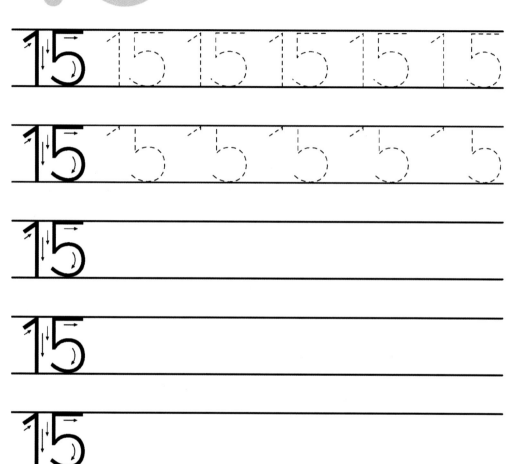

Fifteen

15 15 15 15 15 15

15 15 15 15 15 15

15

15

15

Pterodactyls were actually not dinosaurs, but another type of flying reptiles that lived in the same age.

How are dinosaurs studied?

Fieldwork is only a small part of what paleontologists do. They spend a lot of time classifying specimens and examining their characteristics.

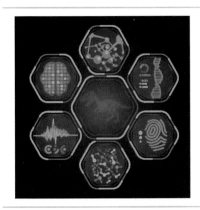

Advanced technology such as CT scans is used to study more about the dinosaur families from their fossils.

16 Sixteen

16 16 16 16 16 16

16

16

16

16

The *fastest dinosaur* was *Orinthomimids*, which could run at speeds of up to 40 miles per hour!

Count the number of T Rexes and the number of Triceratops and put that number in the circles below!

T-Rex ⭕

Triceratops ⭕

38

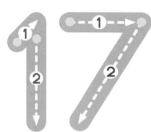

Seventeen

17 17 17 17 17 17 17

17 17 17 17 17 17 17

17

17

17

Stegosaurus **had the smallest brain: it was only** 3 cm long **and weighed just** 75 grams**!**

Color me!

Eighteen

18 18 18 18 18 18

18

18

18

18

Utahraptors were the most cunning dinosaurs. They were powerful, agile, and might have been the most intelligent dinosaurs!

Count how many dinosaurs are in each line!
Write that number in the circle.

Nineteen

19 19 19 19 19 19 19

19 9 9 9 9 9

19

19

19

Dinosaurs *swallowed rocks and stones* while eating. These stayed in their stomachs and helped them *grind up food!*

Can you help this Brachiosaurus get home?

		38	24	78	28	80	48	98
		79	3	4	5	6	7	90
		1	2	24	27	11	8	30
31	32	1	34	98	81	70	74	9	40
41	42	2	64	4	46	63	15	10	50
88	26	53	60	15	14	13	12	11	60
61	62	63	69	16	17	10	68	69	70
26	72	73	84	53	18	19			
95	82	83	84	85	30	20			
91	64	93	94	95	96	97			

Take him through the math maze!

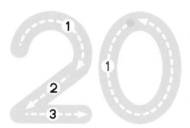

Twenty

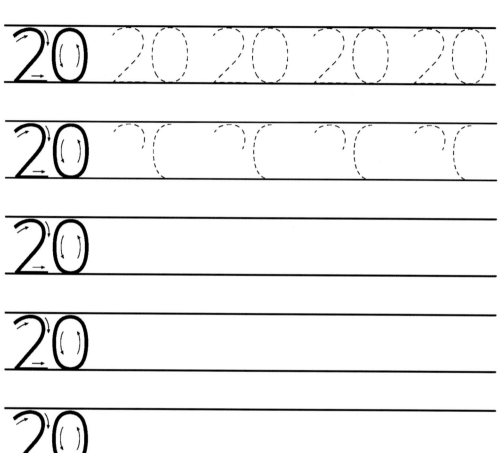

20 20 20 20 20 20

20 20 20 20 20 20

20

20

20

The colors of dinosaurs are a mystery since there was no human alive at that time.

Fill in the missing numbers!

46

Cut out the bottom dinosaur strips and glue the pieces back on to bring this dinosaur skeleton back to life!

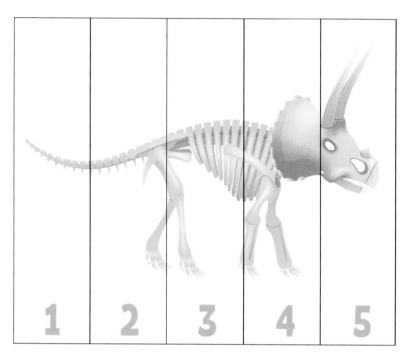

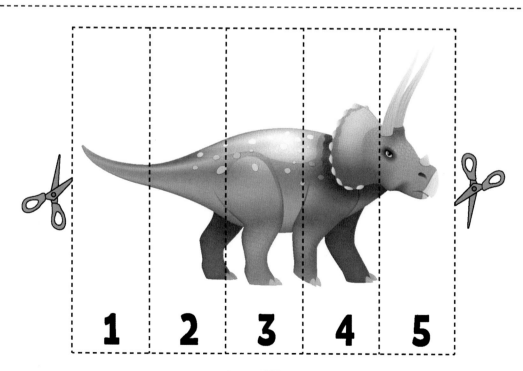

Call a friend! Play with a dice and see who finishes first. There are shortcuts!

LEARN NUMBERS
WITH DINOSAURS

Made in the USA
Monee, IL
18 July 2021

73839505R00033